The Young
SHERLOCK HOLMES
ADVENTURES

CW00530804

MARKOSIA

HAYENA STUDIOS
2010

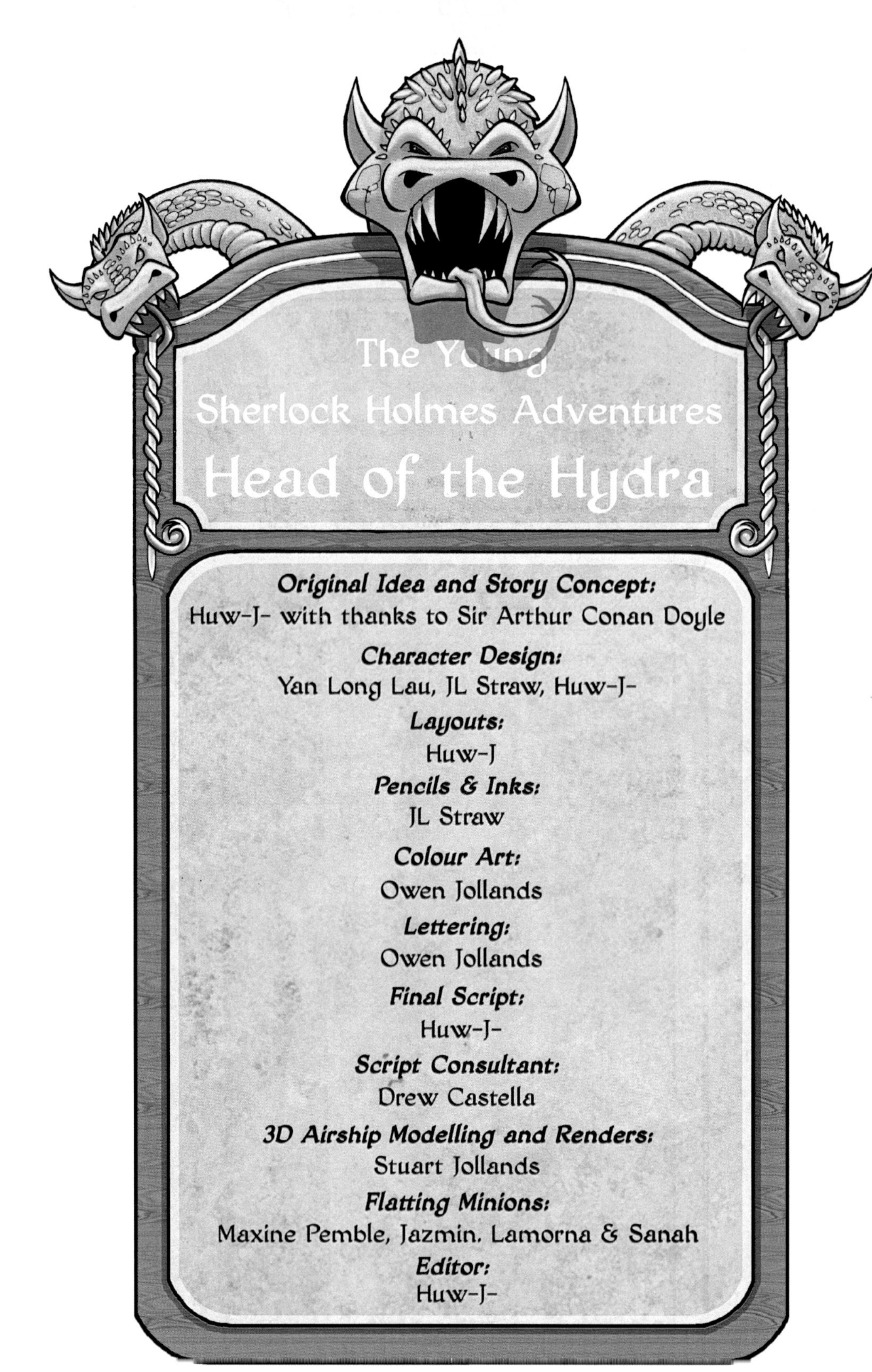

The Young Sherlock Holmes Adventures
Head of the Hydra

Original Idea and Story Concept:
Huw-J- with thanks to Sir Arthur Conan Doyle

Character Design:
Yan Long Lau, JL Straw, Huw-J-

Layouts:
Huw-J

Pencils & Inks:
JL Straw

Colour Art:
Owen Jollands

Lettering:
Owen Jollands

Final Script:
Huw-J-

Script Consultant:
Drew Castella

3D Airship Modelling and Renders:
Stuart Jollands

Flatting Minions:
Maxine Pemble, Jazmin, Lamorna & Sanah

Editor:
Huw-J-

Published by Markosia Enterprises, Ltd. UK FIRST PRINTING, December 2010.Harry Markos, Director. Printed in the UK.

ORWARD:

N THE YOUNG SHERLOCK HOLMES ADVENTURES - WE MEET UP WITH SHERLOCK BEFORE THE HEIGHT F HIS POWERS, STUDYING AT A BOARDING SCHOOL IN THE HEART OF STEAMPUNK BRITAIN.

HERE'S SOMETHING NASTY UP TO NO GOOD IN THE EAST END OF LONDON. IS IT REALLY A AMPIRE? HOLMES IS NOT SO SURE...

HEN THE JUNIOR DETECTIVE FIRST ROARS INTO VIEW ON A STEAM-POWERED MOTORCYCLE - YOU NOW YOU ARE IN FOR SOMETHING RATHER DIFFERENT. BUT IT'S ALSO CLEAR THAT THE AUTHORS NOW THEIR HOLMES.

E'S BRILLIANT BUT SLIGHTLY SOCIALLY AWKWARD AND LACKING IN EMPATHY AT TIMES (ALTHOUGH OT YET AS JADED AS HE WILL BE IN THE FUTURE). IT'S CLEAR HE CARES FOR HIS FRIENDS.

E PLAYS WITH CLOCKWORK TOYS. HE GETS TO DEMONSTRATE "THE TRICK". BUT LACKING THE IFE EXPERIENCE OF HIS OLDER SELF - IT RATHER BACKFIRES ON HIM.

THIS IS SHERLOCK HOLMES AS A STEAMPUNK GEEK OF ACTION - AND IT WORKS WELL.

FOR THE EAGLE EYED READER THERE'S PLENTY OF THINGS TO REWARD FURTHER INVESTIGATION AS MANY OF THE PANELS HAVE OTHER TOUCHES OF THE CONAN DOYLE ABOUT THEM.

I'LL LEAVE YOU TO FIND THEM.

THERE'S ALSO A FEW RICH HINTS DROPPED OF WHAT'S TO COME IN SUBSEQUENT BOOKS IN THE SERIES.FINALLY, ROUNDING OFF THE BOOK ARE A NICE SET OF SKETCHES AND DESCRIPTIONS OF THE CREATIVE PROCESS.

WITH A BIT OF LUCK - ANY JUNIOR SHERLOCKIANS IN YOUR LIFE WILL BE INSPIRED TO CREATE THEIR OWN COMIC ADVENTURES TO FILL IN THE TIME UNTIL THE NEXT BOOK.

SHERLOCK HOLMES BOOKS .ORG

LONDON - THE STEAM AGE!
BUT THIS IS NOT THE LONDON YOU OR I LEARNT ABOUT IN OUR HISTORY BOOKS - THIS IS THE LONDON DREAMT OF BY BABBAGE...
A LONDON FORGED BY IRON AND STEEL AND THE ALCHEMY OF TECHNOLOGY.
TANDING PROUD IN THE CENTRE OF AN MPIRE THAT CONTINUES TO REIGN ITH AN IRONCLAD FIST.
AN EMPIRE WHO'S RED, WHITE AND BLUE FLAG RISES OVER THE WORLD DRIVEN BY THE STRENGTH OF ITS TECHNOLOGY...
D THE STEEL OF ITS RESOLVE R GOD, QUEEN AND COUNTRY.

BUT EVEN HERE, WHILE THE MEN OF LETTERS AND THEIR FAMILIES STROLL THROUGH THE BALMY SUMMER EVENINGS...
DEEP IN THE DARK, DIRTY UNDERBELLY OF TH
CITY - DARKNESS AND HOPELESSNESS STIR -
AND RAISE THEIR HEADS -
GREEDILY COVETING THE WHITE MARBLE HALLS AND STAINED GLASS WINDOWS THAT RAISE SO HIGH ABOVE THEM.

HERE PLANS ARE LAID AND HATE IS FUELLED.

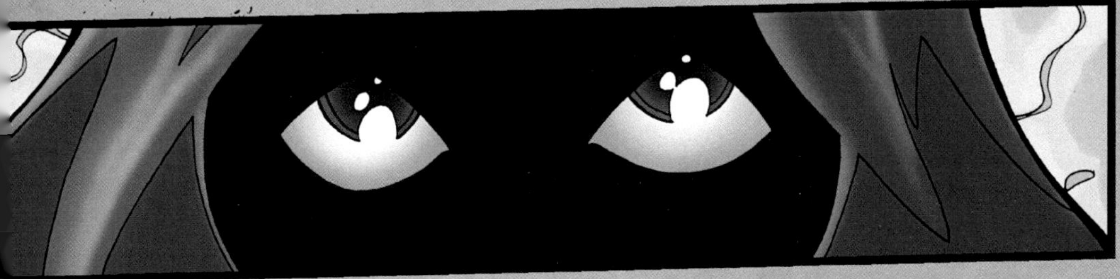

D HERE ARE THE DARK ENTS OF CHAOS.
EAST INDIA
WEST INDIA DARKLANDS

PURSUED AS THEY MELT INTO THE SHADOWS OF THE NIGHT.
AND TONIGHT A HUNTER IS ABROAD...
WEST INDIA DA

HASING A DEADLY PREY.
OWL!
IT'S NOT WORTH IT, YOU KNOW.
IT'S BEEN A MERRY CHASE THROUGH THE SLUMS BUT THERE'S *NOWHERE* LEFT TO RUN!

HOLMES!
YOU HAVE DOGGED ME THROUGH THIS CITY...

BUT ARE YOU SURE *YOU* ARE THE CAT AND *I* AM THE MOUSE?
TELL ME, HOW DO YOU KNOW MY PRIZE IS *WORTHLESS* AND MY ROAD AT AN END?

ELEMENTARY.

EXPLAIN *PLEASE?*

GOING INTO THE DARKLANDS AT *THIS HOUR AND* THE ROUTE YOU TOOK -
- MAKES IT CLEAR THAT YOU KNOW THE CITY WELL.

YOU WON'T RISK YOUR LIFE FOR A CASE CARRYING ONLY HALF OF WHAT YOU PURCHASED IN THE SLUMS.

KLUNK

UNLESS YOU CAN CARRY 150 POUNDS AT A STEADY CLIP,
WHICH WOULD BE REMARKABLE FOR A MAN OF YOUR STATURE.

THE FIGURES WERE EASY ENOUGH TO FIND WHEN YOU CONSIDER YOU PAID IN INDIAN SILVER, NOT GOOD ENGLISH GOLD.
SO WHAT IS SO SPECIAL ABOUT A HUNDRED PHOTOGRAPHIC APPARATUS, HIGH GRADE MULCH -

HEH
HEH

- AND TEN YARDS OF STRIPPED COPPER?

?

YOU HAVE NO IMAGINATION HOLMES...

IT SEEMS I HAVE MISJUDGED...
NITRO
NITRO

CLICK-IK

AND THAT ILL BE YOUR DOWNFALL!

NORTH DOCK
FAREWELL!
-SHERLOCK HOLMES!

SHLUUSH

GAAAHH!
EASY HOLMES!
BREATHE!

YOU'RE LUCKY TO BE ALIVE...
COUGH MY BIKE! KAF KAF GET IT!
YOUR BIKE'S GONE HOLMES - IT'S AT THE BOTTOM OF THE THAMES.

WHERE HAVE YOU BEEN?
SEVERAL STEPS BEHIND. I THOUGHT THAT'S HOW YOU PREFERRED IT.

THIS IS SERIOUS BUSINESS.
WE NEED TO WORK TOGETHER NEXT TIME.

YOU - WANT - TO - WORK - TOGETHER?
=NYAGH=
YOUR HEAD - MUST BE - WORSE - THAN IT - LOOKS!
WE'LL BE BACK ON THE TRAIL TOMORROW JAMES.
I NEARLY HAD HIM BEAT THIS TIME!

HE NEARLY HAD YOU BEAT HOLMES! WE NEED TO FIND OUT WHO THIS COWL IS.

WE NEED TO GATHER FACTS! DATA JAMES... WE NEED DATA!
HOW ABOUT WE START BY GETTING YOU BACK TO LONG HALL?

WE'RE ALREADY ON THE LONG HAUL JAMES. THIS IS A TOUGH CASE, I CAN FEEL IT.

MAYBE TOO TOUGH HOLMES, I THINK THIS CASE IS DEAD IN THE WATER NOW.

OUCH!
GO SLOW JAMES! I SEEM TO HAVE A HOLE IN MY SHOE.
IF YOU'D BEEN ANY CLOSER TO THOSE CHARGES YOU'D HAVE A HOLE IN YOUR HEAD, HOLMES!
THOUGH THAT PROBABLY WOULDN'T HAVE HURT YOU TOO MUCH!

MUCH LATER THAT NIGHT AT LONGHALL ACADEMY.

THE MATRON HAD A *FIT* WHEN I SAW HER IN THE FOYER EARLIER.
SHE WAS LOOKING FOR *YOU* HOLMES.

DON'T WORRY MAL. I WILL SPEAK TO HER, BUT WHY ARE YOU UP SO LATE ANYWAY?

OH, I FELT A BIT SICK SO I WENT FOR SOME AIR.

OK, WELL YOU DON'T LOOK SO BAD NOW. ARE YOU FEELING UP TO A SPOT OF STUDY?
WE HAVE THAT ORAL EXAM TOMORROW.

WE'D BETTER GET CRAMMING THEN!
AND YOU ALWAYS WERE BETTER THAN US AT THOSE ETHICAL ESOTERIC STUDIES THAT PROFFESSOR CASTELLA TEACHES MAL.

I'M SURE I COULD MANAGE A BIT OF STUDY. SHALL WE GET SOME TEA AND MAKE A START?

LOOK HOLMES, I'M TIRED, I'LL...
KNOCK KNOCK

HEY JAMES! YOUR FATHER PROFFESSOR MORIARTY IS WAITING IN THE CHAPEL FOR YOU.

MY FATHER? WHAT'S HE DOING HERE?

YOU'D BETTER GO JAMES. WE CAN DO THIS LATER.

TWO DAYS LATER. SATURDAY AFTERNOON.

KNOCK
KNOCK

BOTHER!

Hospital
YOU MAY ENTER.

MAY I HELP YOU?

FELIX LEITER. AT YOUR SERVICE MASTER HOLMES.

WHAT, AY TELL, CAN O FOR YOU SIR?

IT IS RATHER WHAT WE CAN DO FOR YOU, MASTER HOLMES.

FELIX LEITER
TION AGENCY

I AM SURE I DO NOT UNDERSTAND YOUR INTEREST IN ME...
I AM AFTER ALL, MERELY A COLLEGE INTERN...

E COME MASTER HOLMES. YOUR OLVEMENT IN CERTAIN POPULAR CASES HAS BROUGHT YOU TO OUR ATTENTION.

AND YOUR RECENT INCIDENT IN THE DOCKS WAS HARDLY ONE OF SUBTLE DETECTIVE WORK.

LET US JUST SAY THAT WE WISH TO CONSULT WITH YOU IN THE FUTURE.

GOODNIGHT SIR.

JAMES!
WHERE HAVE YOU B
OLD BOY
IT'S BEEN DA

I HAD TO GO WITH MY FATHER...
MY MOTHER WAS TAKEN. THEY FOUND HER BODY NOT FAR FROM WHERE WE WERE THE OTHER NIGHT.
IF I HAD KNOWN..

OH JAMES. I'M SO SORRY... YOUR FATHER MUST BE BESIDE HIMSELF.

IN DUST WE ARE BORN,

EH?

THAT RHYME... IT'S FAMILIAR. MY MOTHER...

INTO DUST WE MUST REST,
SLEEP THE SLEEP OF PASSING,
IN HOPE THAT WE ARE BLESSED.

BLOOD WASHES OUR SINS,
AND SO NEW LIFE BEGINS,
SET FREE FROM THE COILS OF LIFE,

FREE FROM ALL IT'S STRIFE.
THIS IS THE TOY I FOUND OVER ON CHEAPSIDE.

YOU THINK YOUR *MOTHER* KNEW *THIS* RHYME?

AND YOU SAY SHE WAS FOUND NEARBY...

OH *GOD*, WHY WAS *SHE* IN THE DARKLANDS...

LEAVE IT ALONE HOLMES!

BUT JAMES, THIS
GHT BE IMPORTANT TO THE CASE...

THE CASE...
THE CASE CAN GO TO HELL!

JAMES WAIT...
I AM SORRY FOR YOUR LOSS,
BUT IT'S TOO EASY TO BE...
COINCIDENCE.

YOU
ENSITIVE
CLOT!
MY MOTHER
S BEEN KILLED.
URDERED!
- AND
YOU CAN
OF IS YOUR
CASE!
YOU ARE SO ONE DIMENSIONAL!

TEACAKES CHAPS?

WHAT'S GOING ON?
WHAT'S WRONG?

JAMES HAD SOME BAD NEWS, MAL.

BAD NEWS?! I THINK MY MOTHER'S DEATH IS A LITTLE MORE THAN THAT!

BUT JAMES BE HONEST...
YOU HAVEN'T REALLY SEEN HER SINCE YOU WERE SENT HERE.

YOU TOLD ME YOURSELF THAT SHE LEFT YOUR FATHER AFTER YOU CAME TO LONGHALLS.

HOLMES. BE CAREFUL...

YES HOLMES. BE CAREFUL!

YOU MIGHT NOT NOTICE YOUR COLD HEART FREEZING ENTIRELY!

LATER IN PROFESSOR CASTELLA'S LECTURE
TURN TO PAGE THIRTY-TWO OF YOUR BOOKS GENTLEMEN.

HAPS YOUNG MASTER MORIARTY COULD ENLIGHTEN US AS TO THE MEANING OF THE TEXT.

WELL...?

COME ON JAMES...

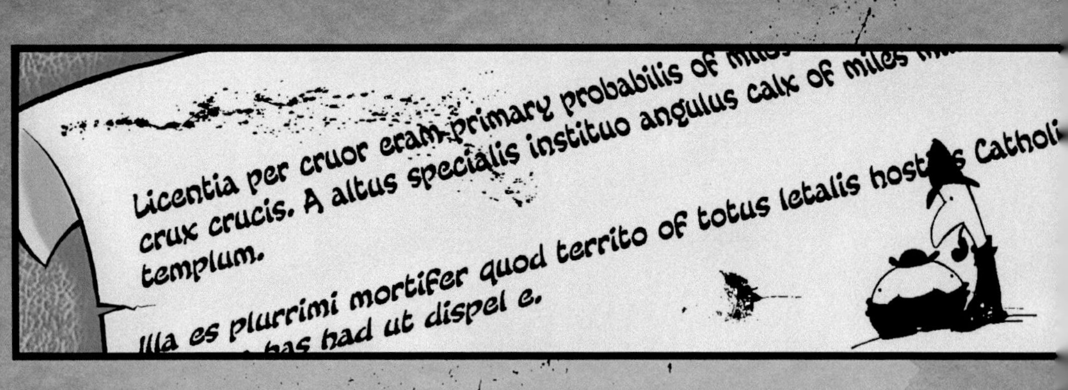
Licentia per cruor eram primary probabilis of miles
crux crucis. A altus specialis instituo angulus calx of miles
templum.

Illa es plurrimi mortifer quod territo of totus letalis host s Catholi
has had ut dispel e.

... ERR ...
...
IT ESCAPES ME, SIR...
OH COME ON JAMES, IT'S SIMPLE. FREEDO THROUGH BLOOD. THE CREDO OF THE KNIGHTS OF THE TRIPLE CROSS.

AGAIN MR HOLMES SHOWS YOU UP MASTER MORIARTY...
YOUR FATH WOULD BE Q APPALLE

I DIDN'T MEAN TO...

NONE THE LESS....

SLAM!

JAMES -- WAIT!

MR HOLMES! SIT DOWN!
WE MAY NOT ALWAYS SEE EYE TO EYE, SIR, BUT JAMES IS MY FRIEND.

AND I AM GOING TO MAKE SURE HE IS ALRIGHT.

JAMES?
Houses of Parliament
Westminster Abbey
River
Thames
Hospital
Babbage Museum

WHERE THE DUCE COULD HE HAVE GONE?

MAYBE...

HEY HOLMES
CHETAN'S COME
FROM HER TRIP
HER FATHER

OFESSOR MISHRA'S HOME? THOUGHT HE WAS STAYING IN INDIA FOR SIX MONTHS.

IT'S NICE TO SEE YOU AGAIN CHETAN.
I SUPPOSE JAMES WILL BE HAPPY.

IF HE COMES BACK.
THEY FOUND YOUR MOTHERS BODY!
OUR DESIGN WAS ACCEPTED
I Love you James
this is for the best...

I DON'T LIKE THIS PLACE.
YOU WOULD LIKE IT *LESS* AT NIGHT, MAL.
POLUS IN

ACTUALLY YOU'D BE SURPRISED HOLMES.
I QUITE ENJOY THE NIGHT.

HA! IS THAT A BACKBONE YOU'VE GROWN?

OR IS IT JUST TO IMPRESS SOME *USELESS* GIRL?

NOW *QUIET* WHILE I LOOK AROUND...

E ARE NEVER GOING TO FIND HIM IN THE DARK.

I AGREE.
WHY NOT WAIT UNTIL TOMORROW?

TOMORROW!

IF YOU WERE UPSET WOULD YOU FEEL IT WAS RIGHT IF NO ONE CARED TO LOOK FOR YOU UNTIL IT WAS COMFORTABLE FOR THEM?

I WAS JUST THINKING PRACTICALLY...

WHAT DO YOU KNOW ABOUT THE PRACTICAL OR THE ELEMENTARY?
YOU STILL BELIEVE IN THE BLOODY INDIAN BOOGIEMAN.

YOU'RE NO USE TO ME AT ALL.

GO HOME.
BOTH OF YOU!

I'LL FIND JAMES ALONE.

I HOPE...

MARCO...

MARCO...

MARCO.

POLO!
Danger
Do Not Cross

OH GOD...
JAMES!

MOTHER? ... FATHER?
MOTHE...
HE'S WAKING UP!
JAMES... CAN YOU HEAR ME?
I HAD SUCH A *TERRIBLE* DREAM!
THE *VAMPIRE!*
I THINK HE HIT HIS HEAD HARDER THAN WE THOUGHT!
NO...
IT

THE MPIRE IS REAL!
?
BUT HE'S NOT A VAMPIRE.
OK, SO HE'S NOT A VAMPIRE, BUT HE IS...
WHICH IS IT?
I DON'T KNOW.
WHATEVER HE IS, HE'S EVIL HOLMES...
IT RADIATED FROM HIM LIKE THE COLD OF MID WINTER.

BUT... BUT THIS MAKES NO SENSE AT ALL,
THERE WAS SOMETHING FAMILIAR ABOUT HIM,
SOMETHING I COULDN'T QUITE TOUCH.

IT'S LIKE HE WAS A GHOST...
BUT ONE I SHOULD KNOW. HE ACTED AS IF HE KNEW ME.
BUT HE COULDN'T, COULD HE?

STARTED TO SPEAK IN
SPING BREATHS ABOUT
OOD.

HE RECITED THE RHYME.

THE ONE FROM THE TOY.

HOLMES, YOU WERE RIGHT.
YOU WERE RIGHT.
MY MOTHER WAS MIXED UP IN THIS.

HE STOOD LIKE SOME KIND OF KING RAT...

HE TOLD ME I WAS NOT YET WORTHY OF THE BLOOD OATH...
THAT I WAS WEAK.
FRAGILE
FRAGILE GLASS

THAT I WAS STILL TAINTED,

WITH THE WEAK BLOOD OF MY MOTHER.
FRAGIL

THAT IS WHY SHE HAD TO DIE. SO THAT I COULD ACHIEVE MY POTENTIAL.

RIED IN MY ANGER
FIGHT HIM.

HE CALLED
PATHETIC...

NOT WORTH *HIS* ATTENTION.
I WAS THE *WRONG* CHOICE.

I WAS NOT THE CHOSEN ONE...
JUST A WORTHLE WHELP.

WHAT DID HE MEAN B THE CHOSEN ONE?

I HAVE NO IDEA... BUT HOLMES, YOU WERE RIGHT!
YOU WERE UPSET JAMES, I CAN UNDERSTAND YOUR BRASHNESS, BUT WE HAVE BOTH NOW SEEN LUCK, RATHER THAN OUR WITS, SAVE US THIS WEEK.
I AM SORRY...
LET NO MORE BE SAID OF IT.

WELL NOW THAT'S ALL SORTED, WHO'S FOR SOME TASTY NOSH?

HREE NIGHTS LATER -- LONG HALLS.

click

THE WOMAN GETS STRANGER AND STRANGER!

SHE'S MEDITATING ON HER SHAKRAS!

SOME CRAZY INDIAN STUFF.

I WAS TRYING TO CLEAR MY SPIRIT AND FILL MY TEMPLE WITH GOOD VIBRATIONS.
SOMETHING YOU, MASTER HOLMES, WILL LIKELY NEVER UNDERSTAND!
WELL I UNDERSTAND YOU COULD GO FILL A POT WITH TEA!
STUNNINGLY GOOD IDEA HOLMES. IT'S ABOUT TIME WE HAD SOME TEA.
THAT'S YOUR SPECIAL JOB ISN'T IT MALACHI?
MAKING TEA?
=OUCH= THIS COBRA BITES AFTER ALL.
I'M WORTH MORE THAN JUST SOME TEA WALLAH!

YOU SHOULD BE MORE MINDFUL OF YOUR SPIRITUALITY MALACHI. I FEEL MUCH DARKNESS ABOUT YOU.

AND AS FOR YOU HOLMES...

YOU NEED TO GET A BIGGER WORLD VIEW.
YOU'RE ALWAYS TOO BOTHERED WITH THE SMALL DETAILS.

DAMN HAT GIRL. S TOO SMART UTHED FOR HER OWN GOOD.

IM... JUST GOING OUT FOR A BREATH OF FRESH AIR, MAL. DO TRY NOT TO RUN INTO THE MATRON IF YOU FEEL SICK TONIGHT.
GOOD CHAP.

I SHAN'T BE LONG.
LONG HA
FOR

AND SO THROUGH THE STREETS OF THE EAST END,
AND ITS DICKENSIAN DENZINES.
GIRLS
STEAM

INTO THE OLD INDIAN QUARTER,

WHERE A PROFESSORS DAUGHTER SEEMS
TO BE TREATED LIKE A CELEBRITY.

CELEBRITY...

QUITE A FOLLOWING.

AND AS THE NIGHT IS FILLED
WITH AN EXOTIC RHYTHM,
A CURTAIN RISES.

HOOOOOH
OH
OOOOH

TO REVEAL A GODDESS.

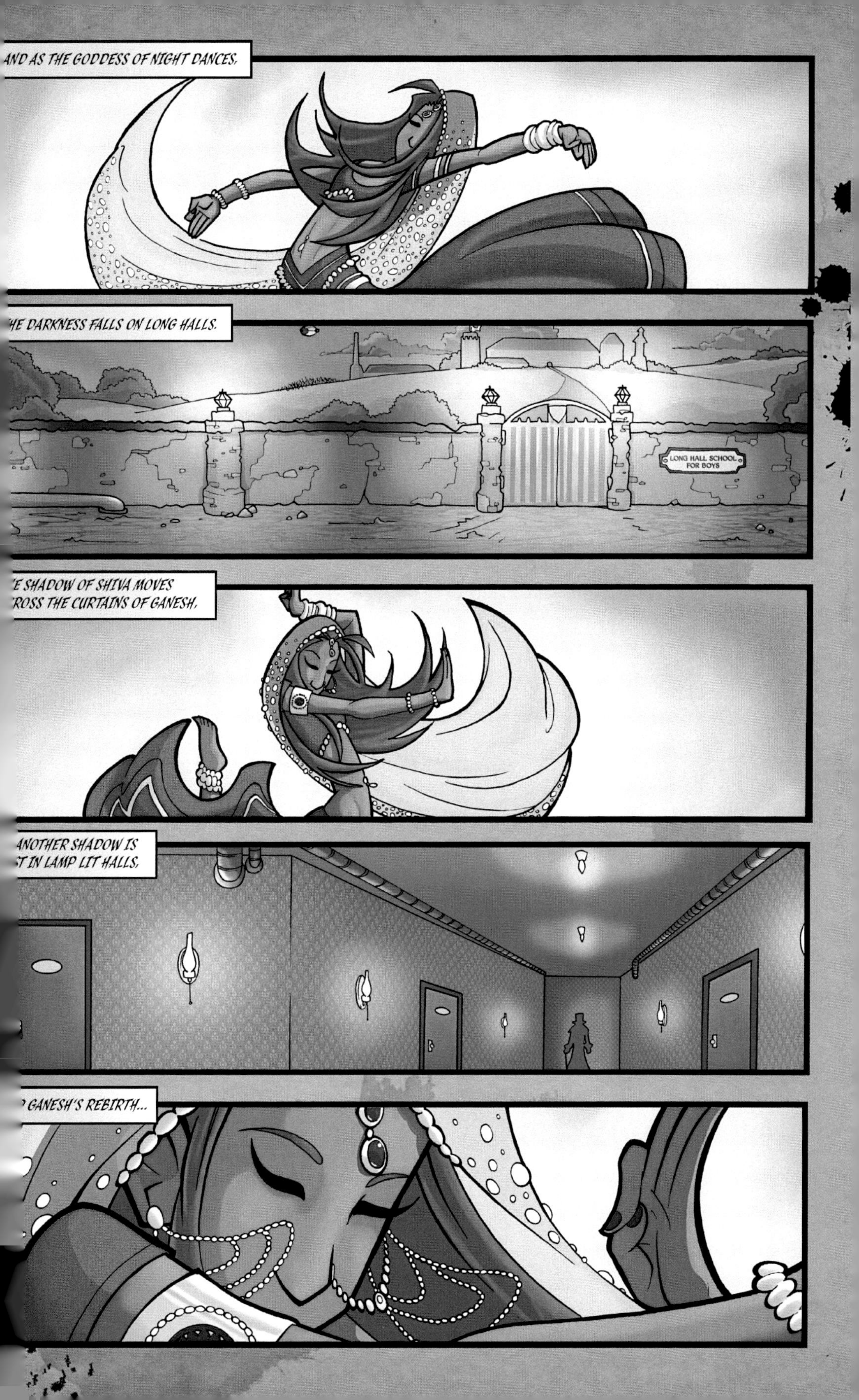
AND AS THE GODDESS OF NIGHT DANCES,
HE DARKNESS FALLS ON LONG HALLS.
LONG HALL SCHOOL FOR BOYS
E SHADOW OF SHIVA MOVES
CROSS THE CURTAINS OF GANESH,
ANOTHER SHADOW IS
ST IN LAMP LIT HALLS,
GANESH'S REBIRTH...

A SHARD OF LIGHT,
212B
IS THRUST OPEN LIKE A DOORWAY TO THE SOUL.
AS PLANS ARE LAID FOR THE CHOSEN,
TO DANCE THE FINAL DANCE!

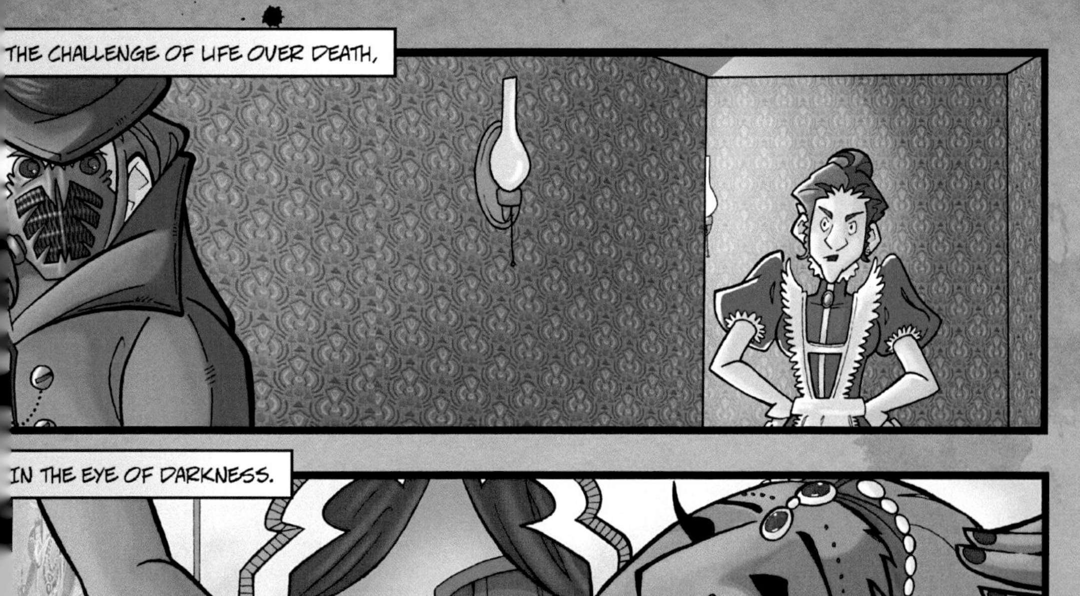
THE CHALLENGE OF LIFE OVER DEATH,

IN THE EYE OF DARKNESS.

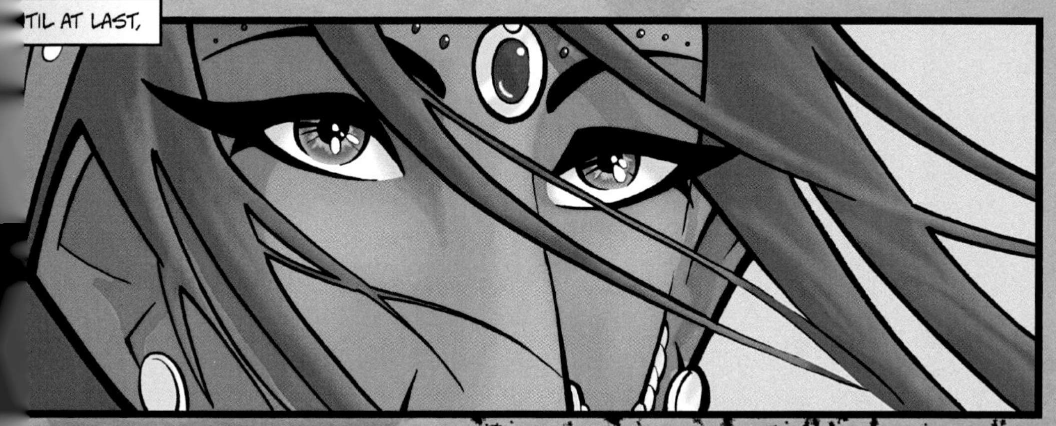
TIL AT LAST,

THE TWO COME FACE...
TO FACE,
AND SACRIFICE IS DEMANDED,
AS THE MUSIC AND DANCE OF LIFE...
ABRUPTLY STOPS, AND THE CURTAIN FALLS.
THE HERO RETREATS,...
INTO THE NIGHT...

ONGHALLS, LATER THAT NIGHT.

PEELERS? WHAT DO *THEY* WANT HERE?

WHATS GOING ON?

I'M *AFRAID* YOU CAN GO *NO* FURTHER, YOUNG SIR.
BABBAGE HALLS

BUT I LIVE HERE!

ALL BOYS ARE TO REPORT TO THE MAIN HALL.

I NEED TO GET TO MY ROOM.
OI! COME 'ERE YOU LITTLE GIT!

ILL BE DAMNED IF SOMETHINGS HAPPENED AND I WASN'T HERE!

MAL!

'ELLO, WHAT ARE YOU DOING UP HERE?

MATRON!

MY GOD!

LE STRADE! GET THAT BRAT OUT OF HERE!

J G CHALLENGER
DORMITORY
WE ARE TRYING TO CONDUC
A BLASTED INVESTIGATION
HERE.
COME ON LAD.

WAIT...
WHATS THAT?

NOTHING FOR YOU TO MIND LAD.
LICENTIA POR CRUOR

JUST THE
RAMBLINGS
A MAD MA
LICENTIA POR CRUOR

COME ON LAD, JOIN YOUR FRIENDS.

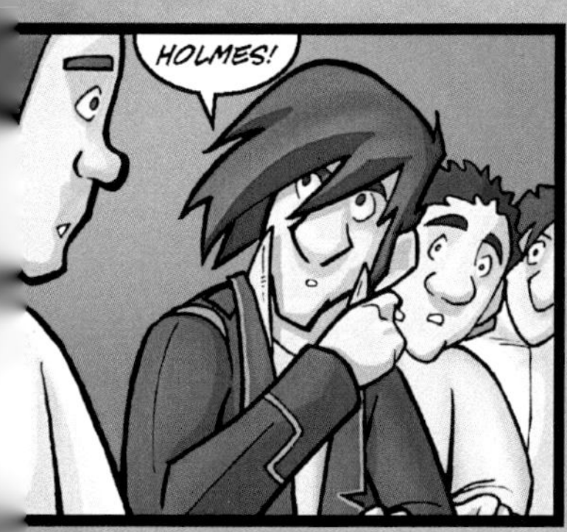

HOLMES!

WHAT'S GOING ON JAMES?
HOW DID THIS HAPPEN?

THE WHISPER IS THAT IT'S THE VAMPIRE.

AND MAL'S MISSING.

AND SO...
I'M NOT GOING TO SIT ON MY HANDS AND WAIT FOR MAL'S BODY TO TURN UP!

WE'RE GOING TO THE DARKLANDS!

WHY THERE?

BECAUSE THAT'S WHERE ALL THE THREADS SEEM TO END.
AND I HAVE JUST REALISED SOMETHING JAMES.

THE OLD ABATTOIR IS THE PERFECT PLACE FOR THE VAMPIRE TO HIDE.
WHY HAVEN'T THE POLICE NOTICED THIS?

MEAT MARKET
MY MOTHER HAD IT CLOSED DOWN.
THEY WONT STOP WATCHING
VAMPYRE

SOMETHING'S NOT RIGHT HERE HOLMES.
YES I AGREE.
EVERYTHING KEEPS COMING BACK TO YOUR MOTHER.

LET'S LOOK INSIDE...

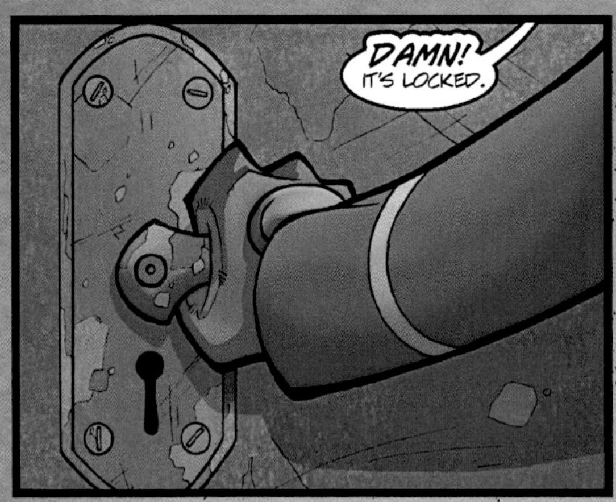
DAMN! IT'S LOCKED.

MAYBE IT'S FOR THE BEST.
MY GRANDFATHER WAS QUITE MAD.

AND I AM AS MAD AS A FOX...
DO YOU REMEMBER MY IDEA FOR A PNEUMATIC SCREWDRIVER?

YOU THINK THAT WILL OPEN IT?

LETS SEE...
KLIK
KLIK

VOILA!
KRAANK

IT'S COLD. SOMEONE HAS STARTED UP THE COOLER SYSTEM.

GET AWAY.... DEATH LIVES HERE!

WHA...
WHATS THAT...

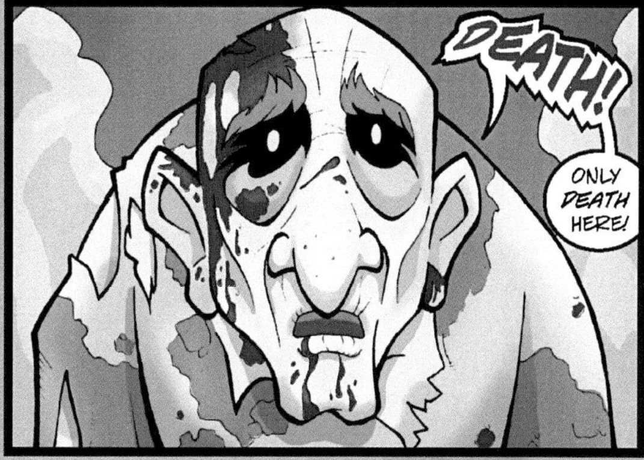
DEATH!
ONLY DEATH HERE!

LOOK... HIS BACK!
DEATH AND DESPAIR!

WHAT'S BEEN DONE TO HIM?

THEM!

THE VAGRANTS... SOMEONE HAS BEEN EXPERIMENTING ON THEM.

YOUR TALENT FOR STATING THE OBVIOUS IS STUNNING!

BUT YOU COULD NEVER SEE PAST THE OBVIOUS.

MAL?

YES! MAL!
AT LAST YOU ACTUALLY SEE SOMETHING FURTHER THAN YOUR OWN NOSE.

BUT... WE CAME TO FIND YOU AND RESCUE YOU... IT WAS YOU ALL ALONG? DID YOU KILL MATRON?

THAT OLD SOW? NO. I MERELY HAD THE PRIVILEGE OF WATCHING.

I'VE BEEN CHOSEN TO ASCEND!

WHEREAS YOU HOLMES, AND ESPECIALLY YOU JAMES, HAVE BEEN DISCARDED.

YOU, JAMES, BY YOUR OWN... -URK-
QUIET WHELP!

YOU TALK TOO MUCH...

MAL!

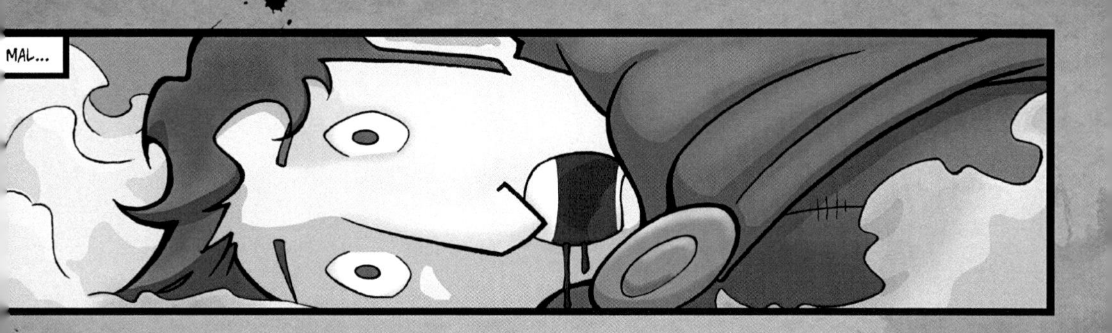
MAL...

NO!

NO!

YOU'RE NOT GOING TO FOOL ME WITH YOUR MASK AND THEATRICS!

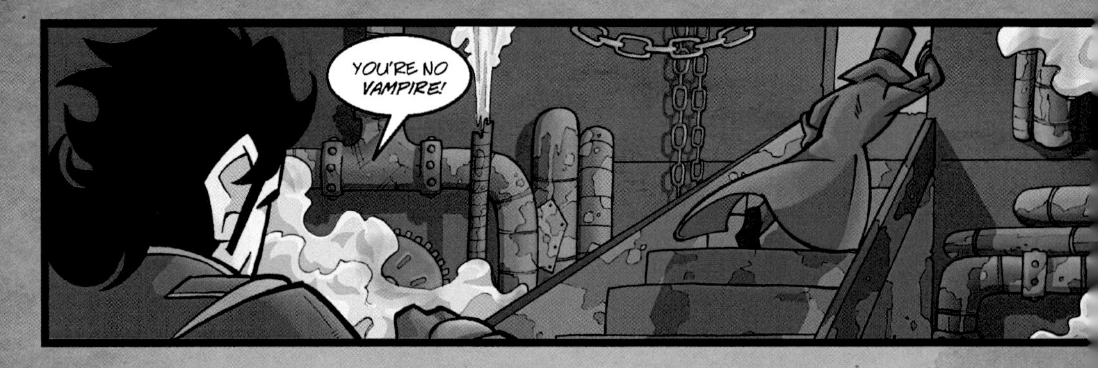
YOU'RE NO VAMPIRE!

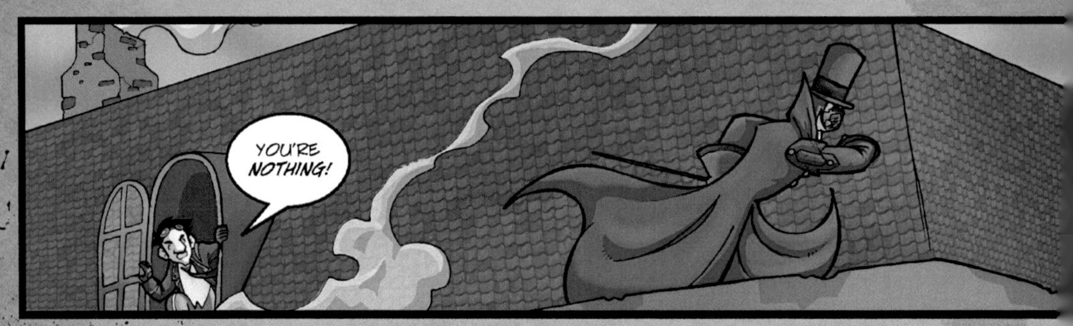
YOU'RE NOTHING!

NOTHING BUT A MURDERER!

A MAD MAN WITH NOWHERE LEFT TO RUN!

AND I KNOW WHO YOU ARE UNDER THAT MASK...

PROFESSOR!

YOU'LL PAY FOR WHAT YOU HAVE DONE!

I WILL SEE YOU HANG!
BOY...

SHUT UP...
HOLMES!

AND DIE!

NOOOOO!

JAMES WAIT!

OH GOD... JAMES.
AAARRRGH!

HE DESERVED IT HOLMES.

HE DESERVED TO DIE.

NO JAMES.

THE VAMPIRE... WAS YOUR FATHER-

ESSOR
RIATY!

COLLIERS HILL CEMETARY.
RÉQUIEM ÆTERNAM DONA EI, DÓMINE.
ET LUX PERPÉTUA LÚCEAT EI.
REQUIÉSCAT IN PACE.
AMEN.

ANIMA EJUS, ET ÁNIMÆ ÓMNIUM FIDÉLIUM DEFUNCTÓRUM,
HOLY
PER MISERICÓRDIAM DEI REQUIÉSCANT IN PACE.
AMEN.

ASHES TO ASHES,

DUST TO DUST,

IN TH
NAME OF
FATHE

THE SON AND THE HOLY GHOST.
MALACHI SUMMERLEE
1890 - 1905
LOVING SON & LOYAL FRIEND

I THOUGHT YOU'D BE AT YOUR FATHERS FUNERAL.

NO.

I HAD THE BODY PUT IN A PAUPERS GRAVE.

POOR MAL.
MY FATHER *DROVE* HIM OVER THE EDGE.

BOY HAS AND *GUSTO* MY LADY.

HE WILL FIT *THE REVOLUTIONS* PLANS ABLEY.
-SOB- AND *MAL*- DID HE FIT THE PLAN TOO?

TWO WEEKS LATER. AS WINTER RAIN WASHES AWAY THE AUTUMN LEAVES.

HEY CHAPS!

I'M YOUR NEW ROOMIE.
WATSON'S THE NAME...

RULE BRITANNIA
STEAM & STEEL
FORGING THE EMPIRE
ds 2010

FROM THE PEN OF HUW-J-

SIR ARTHUR CONAN DOYLE WROTE:

"IT IS A GREAT THING TO START LIFE WITH A SMALL NUMBER OF REAL GOOD BOOKS, WHICH ARE YOUR VERY OWN."

AFTER FINISHING ALL THE ART AND PHYSICAL WORK ON THE 1ST OF THE FREEMAN GRAPHIC NOVELS I WANTED TO DO SOMETHING THAT CARRIED THAT SAME SPIRIT OF ADVENTURE, BUT WAS STILL REALLY DIFFERENT; AND SO I SAT WITH A COFFEE MUSING...

SITTING IN MY PORTFOLIO OF BOOKS AND IDEAS THAT NEVER QUITE SAW THE LIGHT DAY WERE FOUR TEST PAGES ABOUT THOSE RASCALS 'THE IRREGULARS', 2ND TIER CHARACTERS IN DOYLES DETECTIVE STORIES. THIS GOT ME THINKING ABOUT THE CO OF DOING A YOUNG (AND PERHAPS EVEN STEAMPUNK) SHERLOCK HOLMES.

AT FIRST YAN AND DREW WERE BROUGHT IN ON THE CONCEPT WITH JANE AND OWEN IN THE WINGS T FINISHING BUT THE DYNAMIC WAS WRONG AND DUE TO CIRCUMSTANCES YAN HAD TO STEP DOWN FR THE ARTISTIC CHORES.

I LOOKED AT THE ART AND THE SCRIPT THAT DREW HAD CREATED ON THE TOP OF MY STORY TEMPL AND BASICALLY RIPPED IT UP TO START AGAIN. IT WASNT THAT ANYTHING THAT HAD BEEN CREATED WA BAD... IT JUST WASNT GOOD ENOUGH.

HARSH WORDS YOU MIGHT THINK BUT THE BOOK YOU HOLD IN YOUR HANDS WOULD BE CONSIDERA DIFFERENT IF I HAD SETTLED FOR THE EASY PATH; THE MEDIOCRE.

AGAIN DOYLE WROTE: "MEDIOCRITY KNOWS NOTHING HIGHER THAN ITSELF ..."

SO WE TOOK THE GUTS OUT AND STARTED AGAIN WITH THE STORY CONCEPT AS A GUIDE AND TAKIN LEAF OUT OF STAN LEE AND JACK KIRBYS METHOD BOOK I CREATED THE LAYOUTS, THE DYNAMICS O VISUALS. THIS THEN GOT PASSED ONTO THE WONDERFUL MISTRESS OF THE PEN JANE. HERE I HAVE SAY, JANE WAS PUT THROUGH SOME OF THE MOST TEAR JERKING MOMENTS AN ARTIST CAN BE PUT THROUGH; RE DRAW AFTER RE DRAW SIMPLY BECAUSE I WANTED / EXPECTED SOMETHING SPECIAL I WAS NOT GOING TO BE SATISFIED UNLESS I GOT IT.

THE COLORING PROCCESS WAS NO LESS TAXING ON POOR OLD OWEN, AS I FORCED HIM TO RE DC AFTER PAGE UNTILL IT LOOKED PERFECT. TO THIER CREDIT THEY DID MAGNIFICENTLY.

BOTH OWEN AND JANE WERE NO STRANGER TO MY METHODS AND MY DRIVE AS THEY HAD BOTH GRADUATED FROM MY MASTERCLASS AND IT WAS THIS THAT TIPPED MY DESCISION TO BRING THEM C BOARD THE PROJECT.

THROUGHOUT THE CREATIVE PROCESS WE EDITED THE ARTWORK VIGOROUSLY, SMALL DETAILS BEIN JUST AS IMPORTANT AS GRAND DRAMA. THEN AFTER THE ART HAD BEEN LAIN TO REST WE SAT WITH PHOTOCOPIES OF EACH PAGE AND SET ABOUT THE SCRIPTING PROCESS, MAKING SURE ALL THE LITT TWISTS AND TURNS MADE SENSE. THEN BACK OVER TO BROW BEATEN OWEN TO LETTER IT AND FIN OFF.

I WONT SAY THAT THIS IS THE WAY TO DO A GRAPHIC NOVEL, WE HAVE ALL LEARNED A LOT, SLEPT A AND FINALLY FALLEN OVER AT THE FINISHING LINE, BUT I CAN SAY I AM PROUD TO HAVE NURTURED AN NOW SEEN THE FRUITS BORNE BY TWO TALENTS THAT ARE NOW AN IRRIPLACEABLE PART OF MY TEAM THE STUDIO.

I LOOK FORWARD TO MANY MORE PROJECTS TOGETHER AND ASK YOU RECOGNISE THE WORK THE AND THE DEDICATION TO EXCELLENCE FROM ALL INVOLVED IN THE BIRTHING OF THIS THE 1ST OF A SE OF ..

THE YOUNG SHERLOCK HOLMES ADVENTURES

HUW-J-
ART YOU GREW UP WITH STUDIOS
AT THE LONDON FILM MUSEUM
2010

HAYENA STUDIOS LTD

HERE ARE THE CONCEPT PAGES THAT STARTED ME THINKING...
I WANTED TO MOVE AWAY FROM THE USUAL STEAM PUNK STYLE WHICH IS SATURATED IN DARKER AND MORE IRON BASED COLORS AND ADD SOME OF THE BRIGHTER TONES THAT VICTORIANS ACTUALLY USED.
IT KIND OF WORKED...
t went wrong ... he escape went vrong...
Bleeding heck the Guvnor is going to kill me
if I survive that is.
NE OF THE THINGS THAT DID RANSFER OVER TO THE YOUNG HERLOCK HOLMES ADVENTURES AS THE USE OF 'AIRSHIPS'
Just one chance ...
here goes nothing!
Lets just hope that the guvno'r was right about Cog bein' a bleedin mechanical wizard..
Or I'm Pavement Pancakes!
g you flippin nius it worked
w how do I get Down?
IN FACT THESE 'AIRSHIPS' WILL PLAY A VERY IMPORTANT PART IN THE SECOND OF THE YOUNG SHERLOCK HOLMES ADVENTURES

THE SECOND BOOK WILL LOOK AT THE WIDER WORLD OF THE EMPIRE THAT WE HAVE SET OU HOLMESIAN ADVENTURES IN.

SPECIFICALLY IT WILL LOOK AT THE POLITICAL MAP OF THE TIM AND THE GREAT STRUGGLE FO POWER WITHIN AND WITHOUT THE EMPIRE.

MUCH AS OUR OWN MODERN DAY WORLD IS BESET BY THE FEARS OF TERRORISM WE WI SEE HOW THE EMPIRE FACES GREAT NUMBER OF THREATS UPRISINGS AS IT HOLDS SWA OVER ITS COLONIES AROUND THE GLOBE.

WITH OF COURSE OUR YOUN IDEALISTIC HOLMES CAUGHT I THE THICK OF THE ADVENTURE

SO FASTEN YOUR BELTS GET READY FOR THE NEXT THRILLING INSTALLMENT OF

"THE YOUNG SHERLOCK HOLMES ADVENTURES"

RAPTORS FALL

THE CREATIVE PROCESS!
Rejecting Huw-J-´s suggestions is often unwise. Here we see his "methods" in action.
the case of the Exploding Chemistry Lab.
Sprout Soup!

HOLMES - INCOGNITO

Notes on The Young Sherlock Holmes.

The opportunity to work on the Young Sherlock Holmes was fantastic, especially so because I love the books.

The first thing I thought when I saw Yan's concept of Sherlock was "Elvis". If you've read this book and didn't think "Elvis" then I'll pat myself on the back! ☺

By far the biggest challenge on this was trying to make it Steam Punk. I have no creativity at all when it comes to techonlogical or mechanical gadgets. ☹

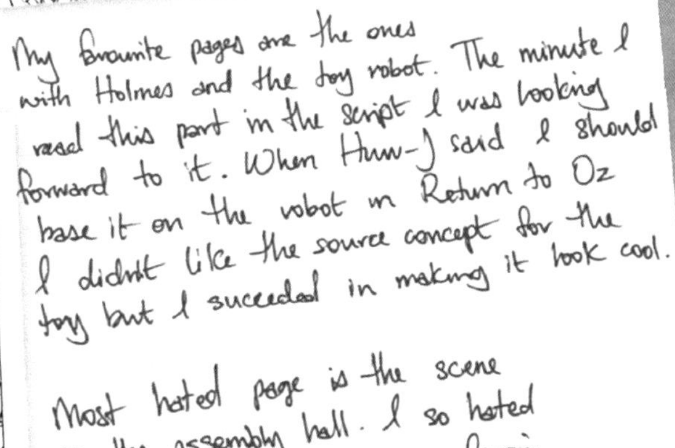

My favourite pages are the ones with Holmes and the toy robot. The minute I read this part in the script I was looking forward to it. When Huw-J said I should base it on the robot in Return to Oz I didn't like the source concept for the toy but I succeeded in making it look cool.

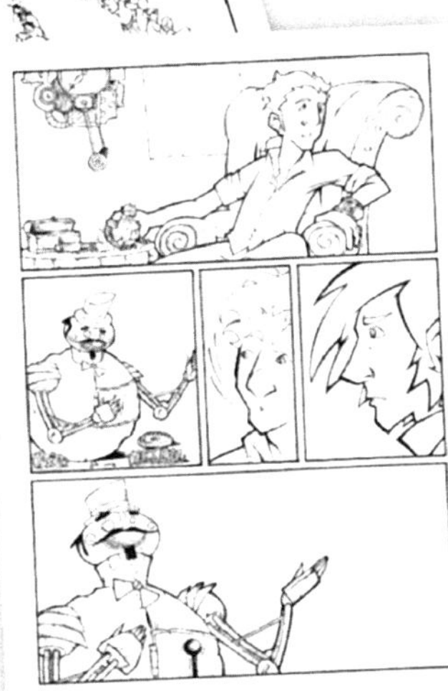

Most hated page is the scene in the assembly hall. I so hated that page 'cos it took so friggin long. I just couldn't get into it but I got there at last with good ridance!

This was a very significant page in this book; it's the first page I inked without Huw-J approving the pencil work first. It's also the page that left Huw-J gobbsmacked. He was really, really, REALLY impressed with this.
I have to say I loved dom all the "extras". Each character had their own story even th their part was to just fill th page.
In comics you have to put across as much emotion as you can. the reader has to feel what's going on through the image which lead to me pulling my face or fist a few times. The more I felt what I was trying to draw the more I could put in. a LOT of thought went into every flick of hand and raise of the eyebrow.
My primary aim when starting on this project was to improve my art work with every page. Quite a challege when comics require consistency. If I've achieved this, then it's another pat on the back for me! The next book will be no different to this rule.
Definately the next Young Sherlock is going to be bigger and better with the art work. Stay Blessed!
JLS.
cola! not coffee
HATE COFFEE

From Masterclass To Team Hayena!

Even before I started on the Masterclass I knew it was the right decision. It wasn't going to be an impersonal classroom setting but a one on one mentoring with an industry expert. It would also provide me with one crucial thing that an ordinary academic setting wouldn't - the chance to get my foot in the comic industry door in real terms.

The Masterclass was an opportunity to learn the ins and outs of the industry and more importantly to discover and build on my strengths, which turned out to be inking. It was the first step to finding myself in my art - a process that continued even when the 10 week course was finished and well into a year after too.

During the Masterclass, we learnt that creating a character starts not with drawing but with writing (something I'm still working on). It is important to know your character in the same way you'd know a friend. They may be fictional, but they are as real as you or I in our minds. The more I drew Sherlock in this book, the more I knew him and his mannerism; the way he'd look at a person or react to a situation and the more I knew him, the easier it became to draw him. And not just Sherlock but all the other characters too. Another point we learnt in the Masterclass was that side characters also help make a story rich. I applied this too when doing Sherlock Holmes even down to the boy in the background pick pocketing on the streets (look closely and you'll find him). I may never draw them again yet when you see them you feel there is a story behind them.

Huw-J often threw us a curve balls during the lessons and he threw me the biggest one when he said I'd have to take over the pencil from Yan on Sherlock Holmes! Yeeiks! Yan is an amazing artist and at first I found it difficult because I was trying to follow the bar set by someone else. But the further into the project I got, the more at ease I became until I was able to make the characters my own. No doubt you'd have noticed the art does improve as the story continues; well now you know why. But it's challenges like these that bring out the best in you and that's what Huw-J did in the Masterclass.

But what I found to be the greatest help when it came to the Masterclass was that I could always go back - and I did! Even when the class was over, I was the only one from my class that continued to visit Huw-J and show him new stuff and he continued to mentor me and give me some practice stuff to do. Eventually he hinted that he had something for me to work on later in the year and when it was time, he brought me into the Sherlock Holmes team. Initially, I was inker but as Yan had to return to China for a bit I took over as penciller and inker.

Ever since, my art has grown leaps and bounds and I'm really, really pleased with how it's turning out. I am however not one to rest on my laurels as I continue to pursue the development of my style and technique. 'You're only as good as your last drawing' was Huw-j's advice to the class and one that continues to influence my work.

Cheers and God Bless!

JL Straw.
TheInkPages

Search TheInkPages on

HAVE YOU SEEN THIS MAN?
LONDON VAMPYRE

Owen's Notes - Colouring and Lettering

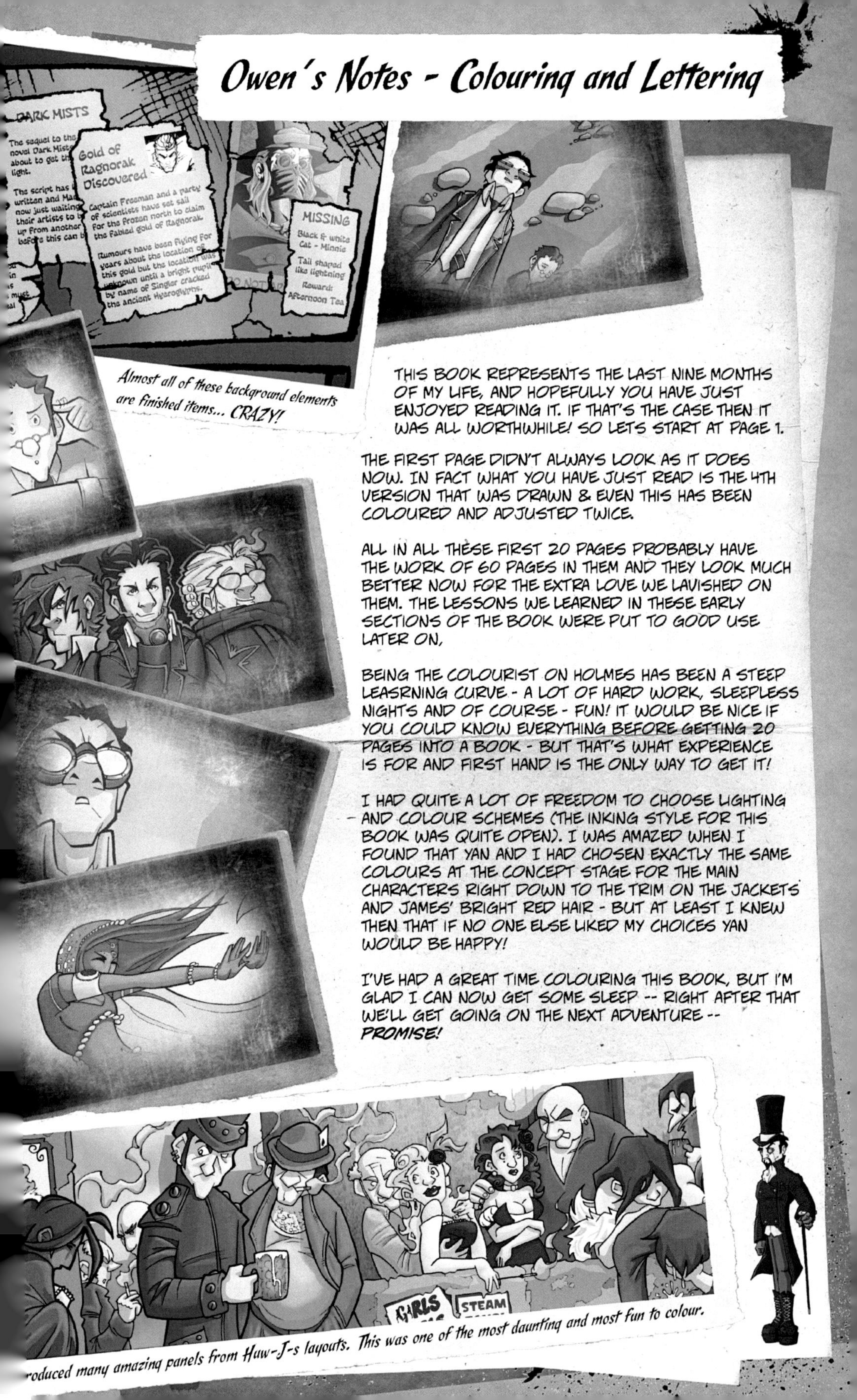

DARK MISTS
Gold of Ragnorak Discovered
Captain Freeman and a party of scientists have set sail for the frozen north to claim the fabled gold of Ragnorak.
Rumours have been flying for years about the location of this gold but the location was unknown until a bright pupil by name of Singler cracked the ancient Hyeroglyphs.
MISSING
Black & white Cat - Minnie
Tail shaped like lightning
Reward: Afternoon Tea
STEAM

Almost all of these background elements are finished items... CRAZY!

THIS BOOK REPRESENTS THE LAST NINE MONTHS OF MY LIFE, AND HOPEFULLY YOU HAVE JUST ENJOYED READING IT. IF THAT'S THE CASE THEN IT WAS ALL WORTHWHILE! SO LETS START AT PAGE 1.

THE FIRST PAGE DIDN'T ALWAYS LOOK AS IT DOES NOW. IN FACT WHAT YOU HAVE JUST READ IS THE 4TH VERSION THAT WAS DRAWN & EVEN THIS HAS BEEN COLOURED AND ADJUSTED TWICE.

ALL IN ALL THESE FIRST 20 PAGES PROBABLY HAVE THE WORK OF 60 PAGES IN THEM AND THEY LOOK MUCH BETTER NOW FOR THE EXTRA LOVE WE LAVISHED ON THEM. THE LESSONS WE LEARNED IN THESE EARLY SECTIONS OF THE BOOK WERE PUT TO GOOD USE LATER ON,

BEING THE COLOURIST ON HOLMES HAS BEEN A STEEP LEASRNING CURVE - A LOT OF HARD WORK, SLEEPLESS NIGHTS AND OF COURSE - FUN! IT WOULD BE NICE IF YOU COULD KNOW EVERYTHING BEFORE GETTING 20 PAGES INTO A BOOK - BUT THAT'S WHAT EXPERIENCE IS FOR AND FIRST HAND IS THE ONLY WAY TO GET IT!

I HAD QUITE A LOT OF FREEDOM TO CHOOSE LIGHTING AND COLOUR SCHEMES (THE INKING STYLE FOR THIS BOOK WAS QUITE OPEN). I WAS AMAZED WHEN I FOUND THAT YAN AND I HAD CHOSEN EXACTLY THE SAME COLOURS AT THE CONCEPT STAGE FOR THE MAIN CHARACTERS RIGHT DOWN TO THE TRIM ON THE JACKETS AND JAMES' BRIGHT RED HAIR - BUT AT LEAST I KNEW THEN THAT IF NO ONE ELSE LIKED MY CHOICES YAN WOULD BE HAPPY!

I'VE HAD A GREAT TIME COLOURING THIS BOOK, BUT I'M GLAD I CAN NOW GET SOME SLEEP -- RIGHT AFTER THAT WE'LL GET GOING ON THE NEXT ADVENTURE -- ***PROMISE!***

...roduced many amazing panels from Huw-J-s layouts. This was one of the most daunting and most fun to colour.

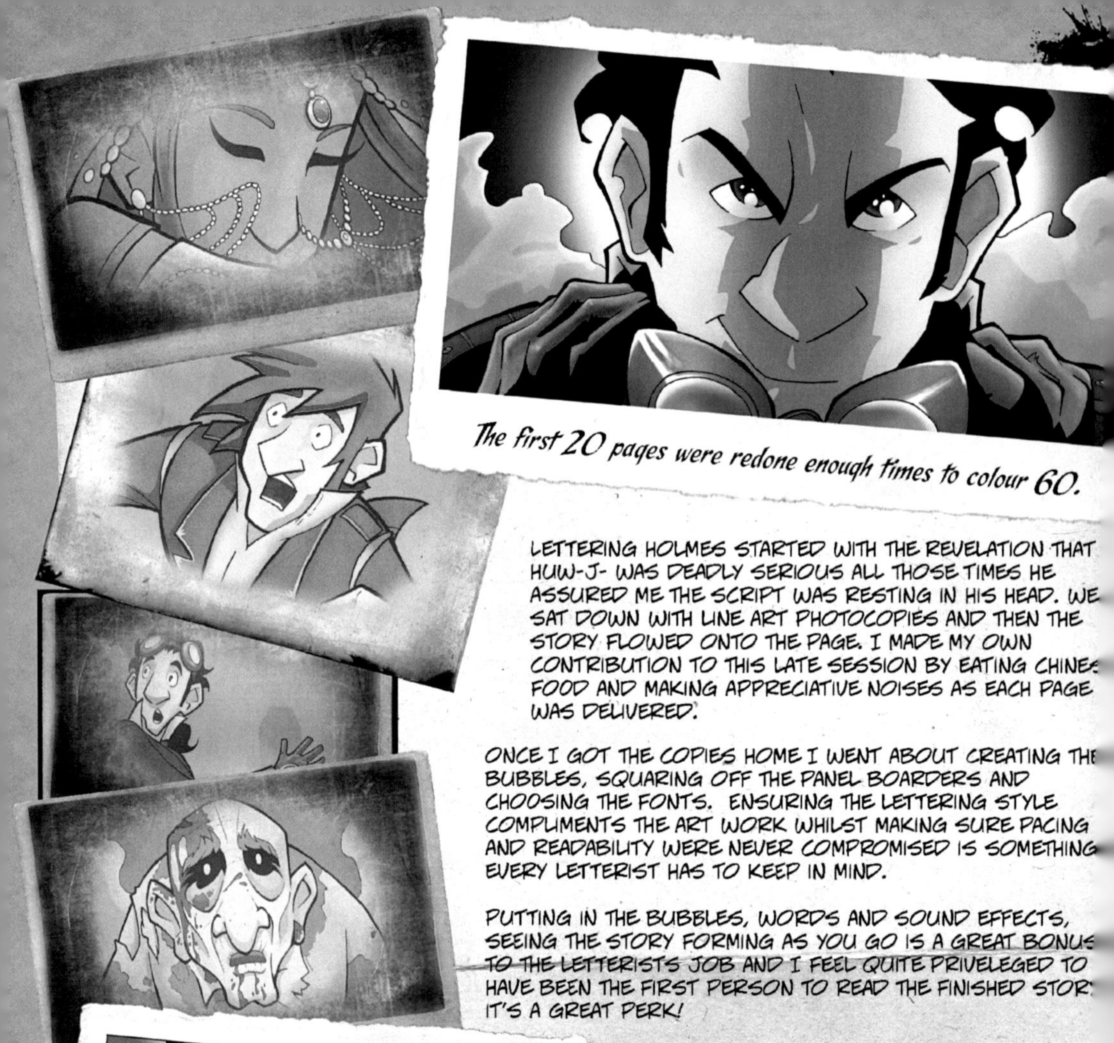

The first 20 pages were redone enough times to colour 60.

LETTERING HOLMES STARTED WITH THE REVELATION THAT HUW-J- WAS DEADLY SERIOUS ALL THOSE TIMES HE ASSURED ME THE SCRIPT WAS RESTING IN HIS HEAD. WE SAT DOWN WITH LINE ART PHOTOCOPIES AND THEN THE STORY FLOWED ONTO THE PAGE. I MADE MY OWN CONTRIBUTION TO THIS LATE SESSION BY EATING CHINES FOOD AND MAKING APPRECIATIVE NOISES AS EACH PAGE WAS DELIVERED.

ONCE I GOT THE COPIES HOME I WENT ABOUT CREATING THE BUBBLES, SQUARING OFF THE PANEL BOARDERS AND CHOOSING THE FONTS. ENSURING THE LETTERING STYLE COMPLIMENTS THE ART WORK WHILST MAKING SURE PACING AND READABILITY WERE NEVER COMPROMISED IS SOMETHING EVERY LETTERIST HAS TO KEEP IN MIND.

PUTTING IN THE BUBBLES, WORDS AND SOUND EFFECTS, SEEING THE STORY FORMING AS YOU GO IS A GREAT BONUS TO THE LETTERISTS JOB AND I FEEL QUITE PRIVELEGED TO HAVE BEEN THE FIRST PERSON TO READ THE FINISHED STOR IT'S A GREAT PERK!

This page set the pace. As soon as this was done, Huw-J- demanded this or better - I had hit my first benchmark.

IT HAS BEEN A LOT OF FUN TO WORK WITH JAN AND HUW-J ON THIS BOOK. THEY NEVER FAIL TO AMAZE ME WITH THEIR ARTISTIC ABILITIES AND BO FREQUENTLY PITCH IN NEW IDEAS AND INTERES TAKES ON WHAT WE WERE DOING.

HUW-J- & JANE ARE ALWAYS PUSHING FOR BE THINGS AND ALL THE LESSONS LEARNED FROM AND FROM MY OWN EXPERIENCES, ARE ENGRAIN IN THE BLOOD AND SWEAT STAINING MY WACOM A TEAM WE'VE HAD A LOT OF MEETINGS AND SP A LOT OF TIME TRYING TO MAKE SURE EVERYTH WAS JUST RIGHT.

I SPENT MY HOLIDAYS FROM MY DAY JOB WORKING WITH HUW-J- IN THE GALLERY ON HOLMES THIS YEAR. IT'S A STRANGE EXPERIENCE BEING IN A STUDIO THAT'S OPEN TO THE PUBLIC AND BEING PART OF AN EXHIBIT, IT'S GREAT TO MEET PEOPLE INTERESTED IN COMICS AND THE CREATIVE INDUSTRIES AND ALTHOUGH IT WASN'T EXACTLY A HOLIDAY - IT WAS DEFINITELY THE BEST WEEKS OF 2010.

There were quite a few panels where I had to think of a way of conveying something I hadn't had to do before.

OUR EXPERIENCE WILL (HOPEFULLY) MAKE THE NEXT ADVENTURE A SMOOTHER RIDE AND A QUICKER JOURNEY. BUT NO MATTER HOW HARD IT GETS I NOW KNOW WHAT IT IS POSSIBLE TO ACHIEVE AND WILL BE PURSUING A FUTURE IN COMICS WITH GREAT CONVICTION AS A MEMBER OF HAYENA STUDIOS.

JANE AND I ARE BOTH PROUD GRADUATES OF THE MASTERCLASS RUN BY HUW-J AND THE GUYS AT "ART YOU GREW UP WITH". ULTIMATELY FOR ME IT IS THE PREPARATION I HAVE DONE THROUGH THE MASTERCLASS THAT ALLOWED ME TO BELIEVE THIS NOVEL WAS POSSIBLE. FAILING SPECTACULARLY IN THE CLASSROOM ENVIRONMENT GAVE ME A LOT OF KNOWLEDGE ON WHAT ***NOT*** TO DO THIS TIME!

AS YODA ONCE SAID - "THERE IS NO TRY, THERE IS ONLY DO; OR DO NOT."

FOR ME THIS BOOK WAS NOT ABOUT TRYING TO DO OUR BEST. IT WAS GOING TO ***BE*** THE BEST WE COULD MAKE IT AT EVERY STAGE AND THAT IS WHAT WE HAVE ACHIEVED. IF WE WERN'T HAPPY WITH A SECTION WE WOULD RE-DO IT UNTIL WE GOT IT RIGHT - EVEN THE FRONT COVER IS THE SECOND FINISHED FRONT COVER AS JANE AND I BOTH THOUGHT WE COULD DO BETTER.

SO ALL THAT'S REALLY LEFT NOW IS TO THANK EVERYONE ELSE THAT MADE THIS BOOK A POSSIBILITY

FIRST THERE IS HARRY - OUR LEGENDARY PUBLISHER WHO TAKES THE RISKS OTHER PUBLISHERS WONT TAKE AND AS A RESULT HAS A STRING OF BIG NAME TALENTS WHO GOT BREAKS WORKING FOR MARKOSIA.

THEN THERE IS ALL THE FRIENDS WHO REMAIN MY FRIENDS - DESPITE THE FACT I'VE LIKELY NOT SEEN THEM FOR THE LAST NINE MONTHS... THANKS TO ALL OF YOU.

FINALLY THERE IS MY VERY OWN SUPERGIRL MAXINE. SHE'S BEEN A NINE MONTH WIDOW OF SHERLOCK HOLMES AND IS GLAD TO NEARLY HAVE ME BACK. THANKS FOR THE SUPPORT AND UNDERSTANDING HONEY.

WITHOUT YOU I WOULDN'T HAVE EVEN MET HUW-J-, LET ALONE WORKED ON THIS BOOK.

FINALLY THANKS TO ALL OF YOU FOR READING AND SUPPORTING OUR BOOK!

TO THE NEXT ADVENTURE!

OWEN - 2010

This was the tester page that I coloured for Huw-J- before starting on The Young Sherlock Holmes Adventures.

The new Imperial master craft Excelsior. I managed to sneak some photoplates from the docks - I have reason to believe this may become a target but it is a mystery as to how one would bring down such a beast of engineering.

Monarch manouvering engine is the
external weak point - without these
and manouvering would be impossible.
Crew and passengers are split between two sections. Officers and luxury guests are in the front "cockpit" dome. Engineering, freight and standard class are in the primary cabin slung under the belly.

hese blue print plates have given me a lead of sorts. The Engineers Huw-J- & tuart could provide me with valuable information. These two must be tracked own - a great deal of lives could be at stake!

Primary Rudder.
Composite Helium Chamber with Modified Steel Super Structure.
Class Mega-Engine.
Class Manouvering Engine.
Monarch manouvering engine is the primary external weak point - without these docking and manouvering would be impossible.
Original Concept Sketch
Imperial Engineers Huw -J- & Stuart
Primary Empire Class Mega-Engine.
and Luxury Passenger
ight and
gineering
ecks.
Standard Clas
Passenger De
Monarch Class Landing and Manouvering Engine.
Crew and passengers are split between two sections. Officers and luxury guests are in the front "cockpit" dome. Engineering, freight and standard class are in the primary cabin slung under the belly.

The Young Sherlock Holmes Sketchbook

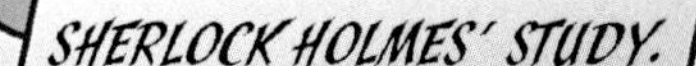

SHERLOCK HOLMES' STUDY.
OH HELLO -- I'M AFRAID YOU'VE CAUGHT ME BEFORE I'M READY.
PLEASE MAKE YOURSELF AT HOME & PERUSE MY SKETCHBOOK...
NOW IF ONLY MAL WERE HERE TO MAKE THE BLASTED TEA!

JAMES' DOODLE WAS COPIED FROM THIS BY PHILIP STRAW AND KEVIN WATTS.
THIS HOUND HAS BEEN DOGGIN
ME FOR MONTHS, I FEAR HE WO
LEAVE ME

Creative Process - Start to Finish

Layouts

Blue line / Pencils

Inks

Flats

Full Colour + Backgrounds

Yan's great Concept Images for Sherlock Holmes and his gadgets set the stage and got imaginations fired!
Hats, Telephones, Penny Farthings and Carriages. Yan's attenetion to detail on these is incredible.

Early Concept Artwork

Holmes - Trading Card

Those Pesky Kids!

the Revenge of Icarus Odbod

o The Next Adventure!